THIS BOOK BELONGS TO

_____

Inside are many mazes

To give you hours of fun

When you reach the end of them

You've finished Level One!

Parents,

if you'd like to see more fun activity books
like this one for your child,
please use the link or QR code below
to leave us a review!

Review.AmazingMazesOne.com

Amazing Mazes for Kids Ages 4-6: Maze Activty Book for Kids | Over 100 Mazes

ISBN: 979-8-9888286-1-7

Contact for permissions: housebooksonline@gmail.com

1

HELP THE BUNNY GET TO THE CARROT!

2

CAN YOU WATER
THE PRETTY FLOWER?

HELP THE CLOWN GET THE BALL. DON'T STEP ON THE STARS!

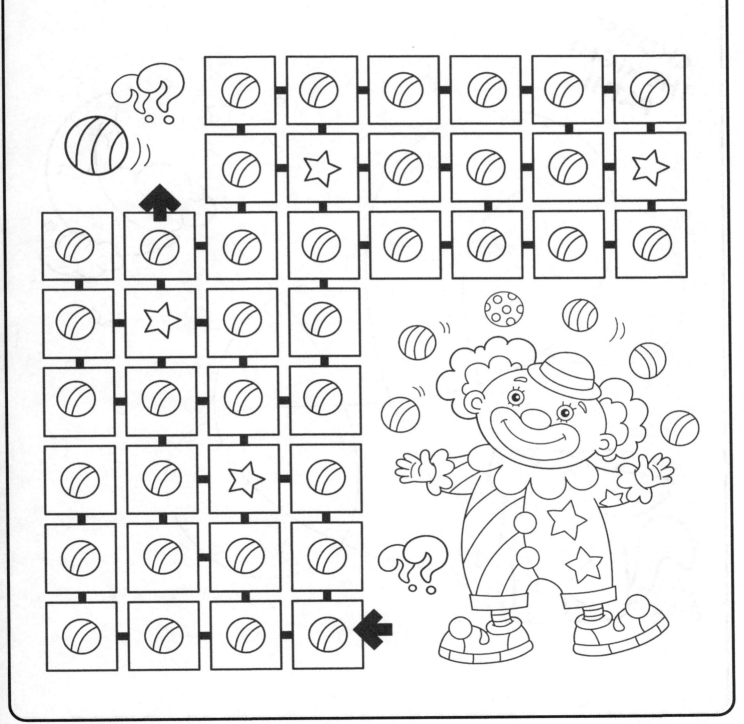

4

CAN LITTLE FOX HOWL TO THE MOON?

CHOOSE THE RIGHT PATH!

5

MAMA DUCK LOST HER BABIES!
HELP HER GATHER THEM.

GRAB A FRIEND . . .

BE THE FIRST TO MATCH EACH VEHICLE TO THE RIGHT PLACE!

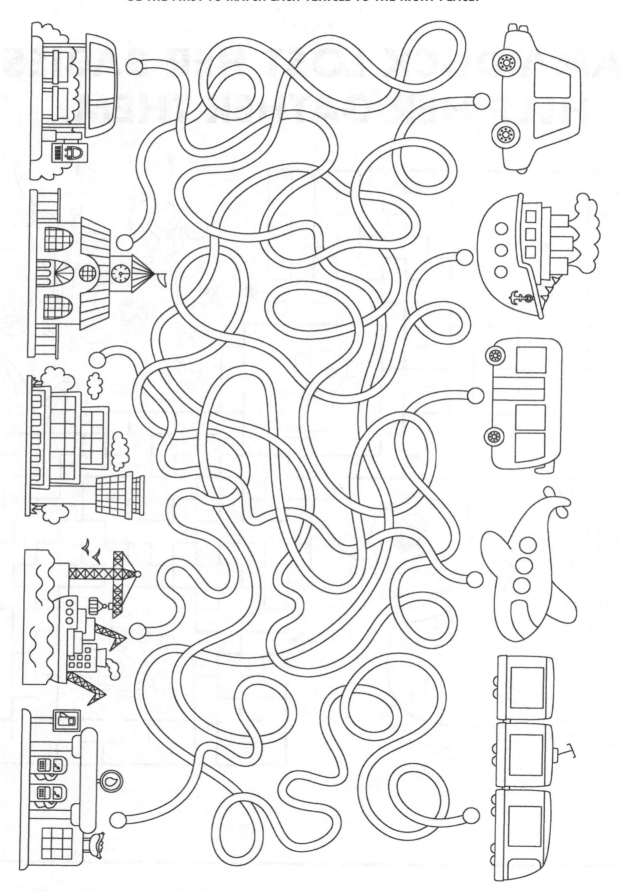

PLAYER ONE

AND RACE TO WIN!

BE THE FIRST TO MATCH EACH VEHICLE TO THE RIGHT PLACE!

PLAYER TWO

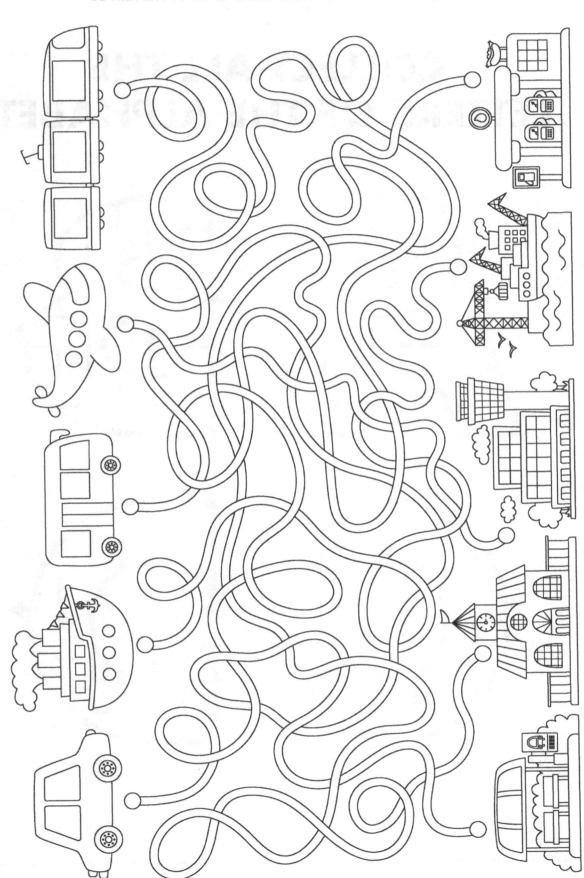

COLLECT ALL THE
LETTERS OF THE ALPHABET.

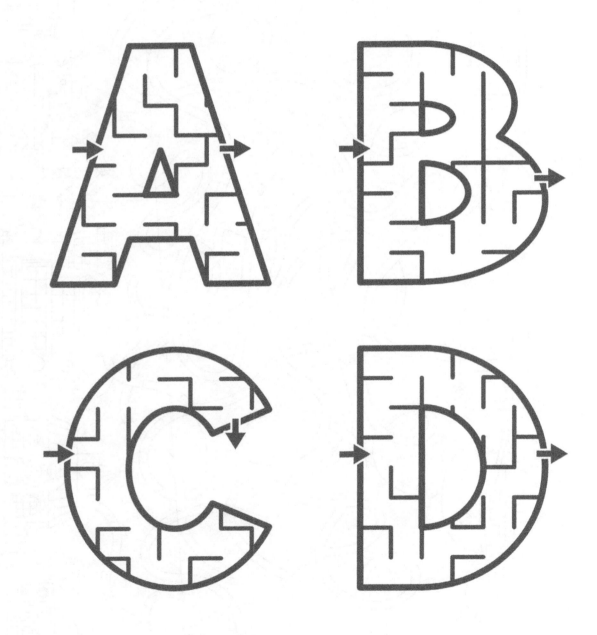

HAVE SOMEONE TIME YOU!

CAN YOU WIN IT IN A MINUTE?

START

FINISH

I DID THIS MAZE IN _____ SECONDS!

ELEPHANT CHALLENGE MAZE

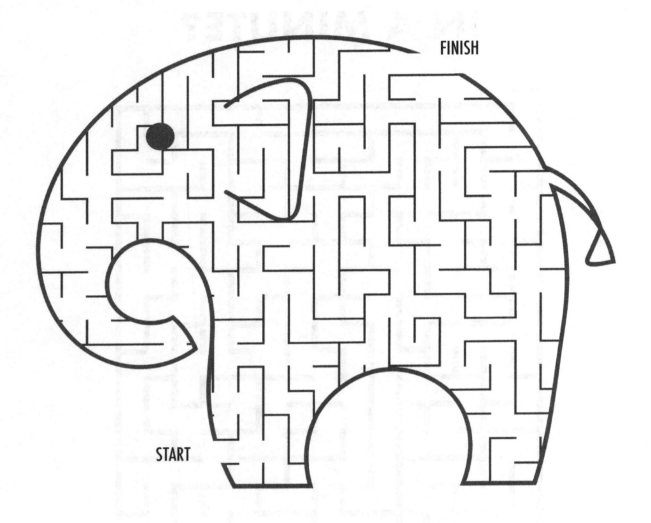

FINISH

START

☐ I MADE IT!

☐ I'LL KEEP TRYING!

LITTLE MOUSE WANTS CHEESE! CAN YOU HELP HIM?

12

HELP LITTLE GORILLA PICK A BANANA.

MOVE THE PUCK TO THE GOAL. DON'T SLIP ON THE ICE!

HELP LITTLE PANDA GET TO THE BAMBOO!

CHOOSE THE RIGHT PATH!

15

HELP LITTLE BEAR
COLLECT ALL THE PRESENTS!

GRAB A FRIEND . . .

PLAYER ONE _____

PLAYER TWO _____

COLLECT ALL THE LETTERS OF THE ALPHABET.

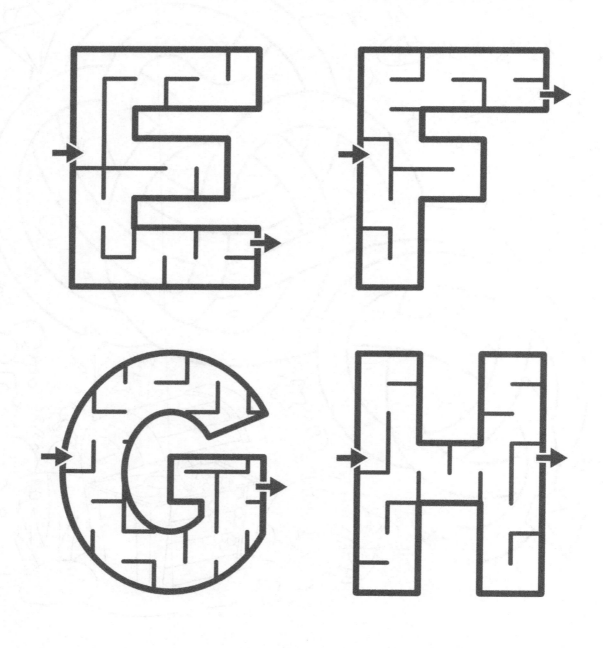

HAVE SOMEONE TIME YOU!

CAN YOU WIN IT IN A MINUTE?

START

FINISH

I DID THIS MAZE IN _____ SECONDS!

SHIP CHALLENGE MAZE

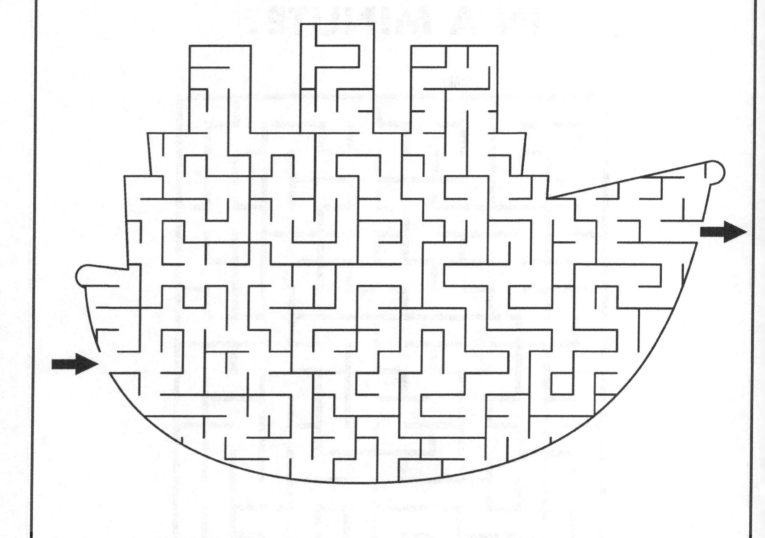

I MADE IT!

I'LL KEEP TRYING!

21

HELP THE GOAT
GET TO THE CABBAGE!

22

CAN THE HELICOPTER FLY?

23

GRAB THE SPRAY & HELP CLEAN! STAY ON THE BUBBLES.

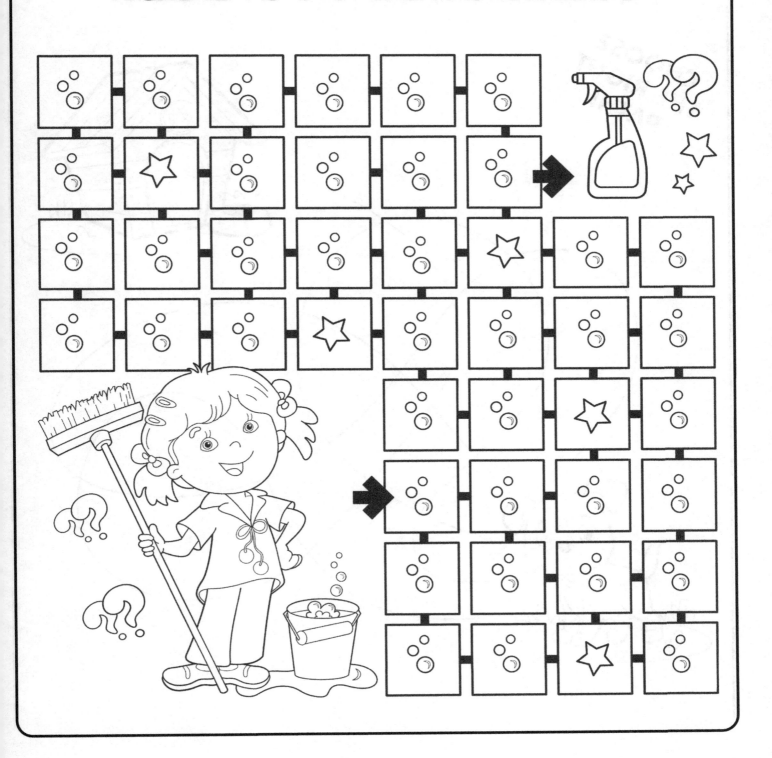

HELP LITTLE PUPPY GET TO THE DOG HOUSE.

CHOOSE THE RIGHT PATH!

HELP THE BEAR FIND EACH HONEY BARREL!

GRAB A FRIEND . . .

BE THE FIRST TO MATCH EACH INSECT TO THE PLANT BELOW IT!

PLAYER ONE

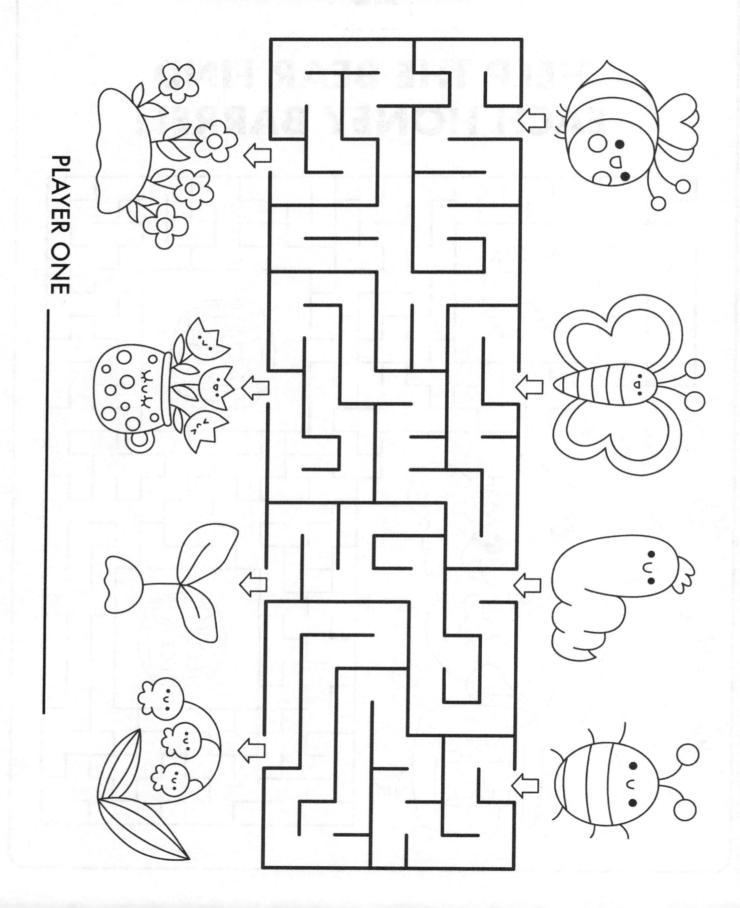

AND RACE TO WIN!

BE THE FIRST TO MATCH EACH INSECT TO THE PLANT BELOW IT!

PLAYER TWO

COLLECT ALL THE LETTERS OF THE ALPHABET.

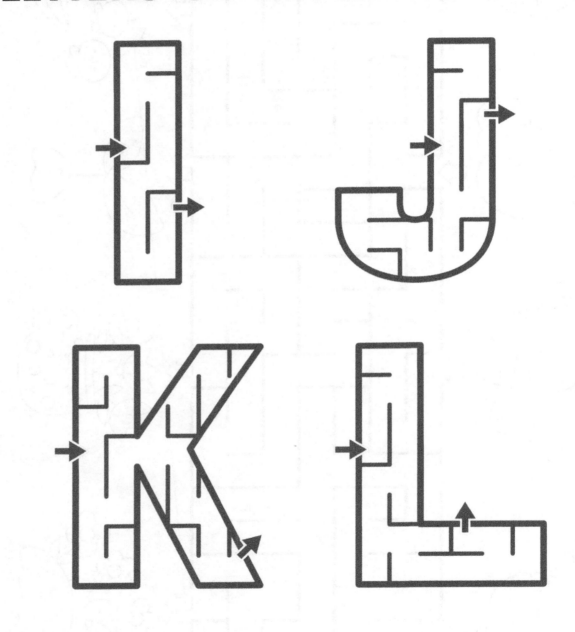

HAVE SOMEONE TIME YOU!

CAN YOU WIN IT IN A MINUTE?

START

FINISH

I DID THIS MAZE IN _____ SECONDS!

FISH CHALLENGE MAZE

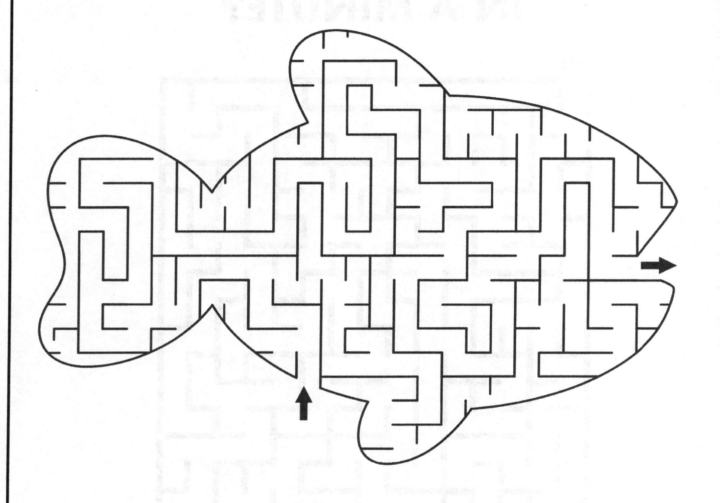

☐ **I MADE IT!**

☐ **I'LL KEEP TRYING!**

31

HELP LITTLE COW
SMELL THE PRETTY FLOWER!

32

CAN THE WORM GET TO THE APPLE?

33

HELP SERVE THE SOUP. DON'T STEP ON THE BREAD!

CAN THE ARROW HIT THE BULLSEYE?

CHOOSE THE RIGHT PATH!

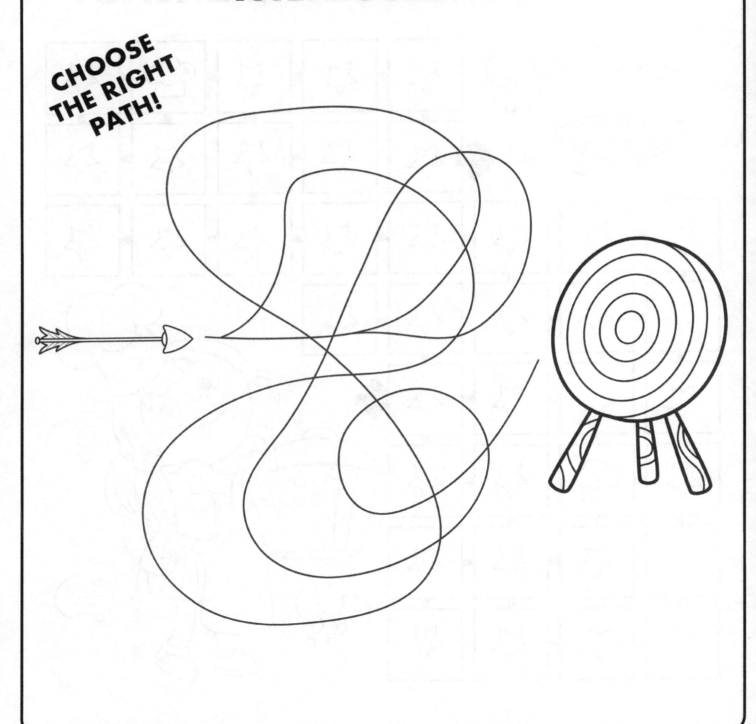

HELP LITTLE MONKEY GRAB THE BANANAS!

GRAB A FRIEND . . .

HELP MR. WORM DELIVER THE HEART! BE QUICK!

PLAYER ONE
_____

AND RACE TO WIN!

HELP MR. WORM DELIVER THE HEART! BE QUICK!

PLAYER TWO

COLLECT ALL THE LETTERS OF THE ALPHABET.

HAVE SOMEONE TIME YOU!

CAN YOU WIN IT IN A MINUTE?

START

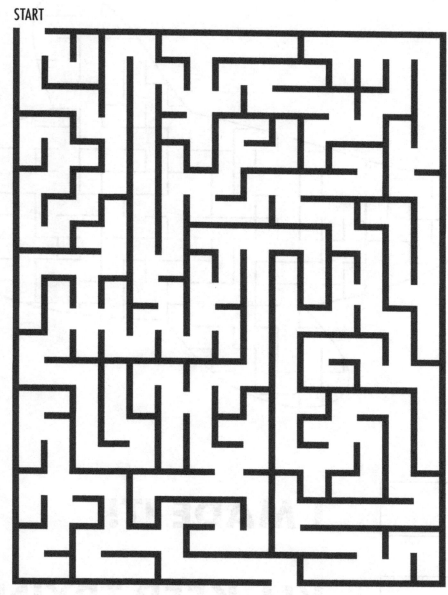

FINISH

I DID THIS MAZE IN _____ SECONDS!

AIRPLANE CHALLENGE MAZE

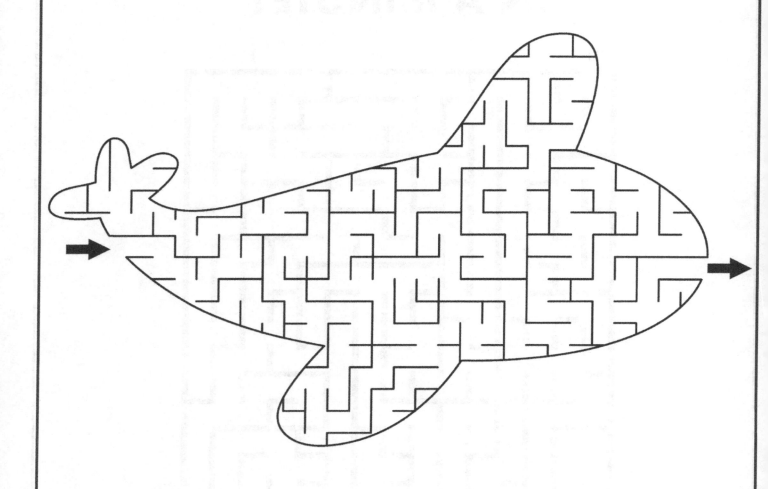

☐ I MADE IT!

☐ I'LL KEEP TRYING!

SCOOP THE FISH OUT OF THE FISH BOWL!

CAN THE SEAL FIND THE FISH?

43

THE ROBOT NEEDS GEARS! DON'T STEP ON THE X'S.

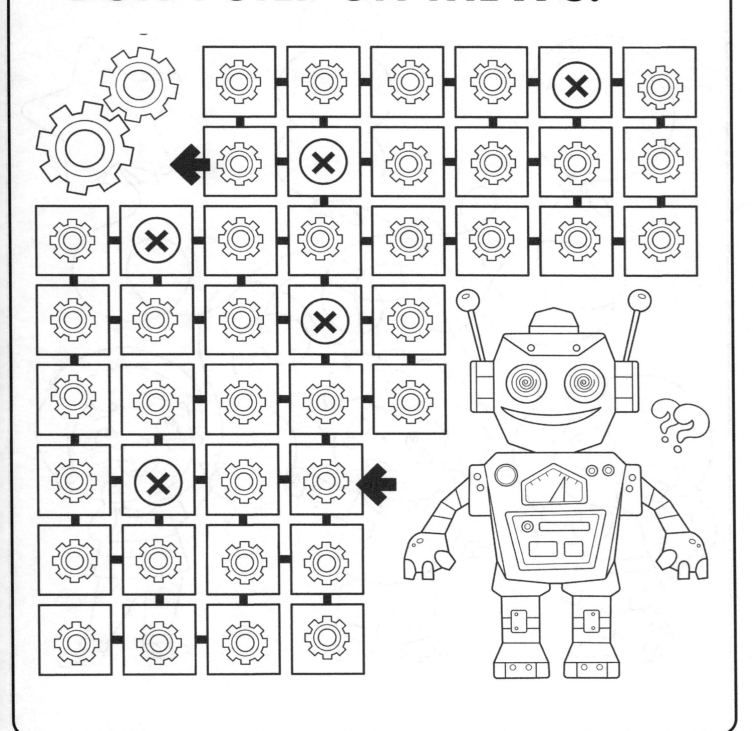

WHO HAS EACH BALLOON?

45

HELP LITTLE FROG JUMP TO EACH LILY PAD!

GRAB A FRIEND . . .

WHICH DOG BELONGS IN THE HOUSE? FIND OUT AS FAST AS YOU CAN!

PLAYER ONE _____

AND RACE TO WIN!

WHICH DOG BELONGS IN THE HOUSE? FIND OUT AS FAST AS YOU CAN!

PLAYER TWO _____

COLLECT ALL THE
LETTERS OF THE ALPHABET.

49

CAN YOU WIN IT IN A MINUTE?

START

FINISH

I DID THIS MAZE IN _____ SECONDS!

ICE CREAM CHALLENGE MAZE

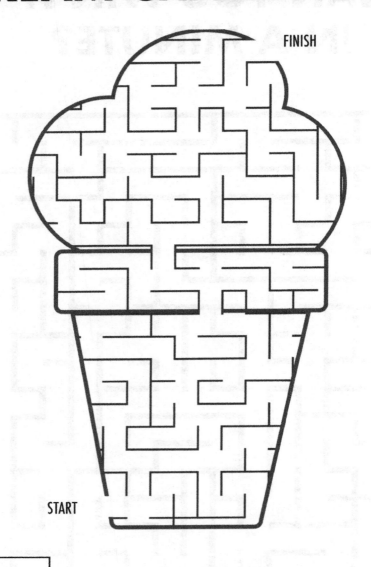

FINISH

START

☐ **I MADE IT!**

☐ **I'LL KEEP TRYING!**

HELP LITTLE KITTEN GET THE YARN!

CAN LITTLE RABBIT FIND THE CARROT?

CAN YOU SCORE A GOAL?
STAY ON THE STARS.

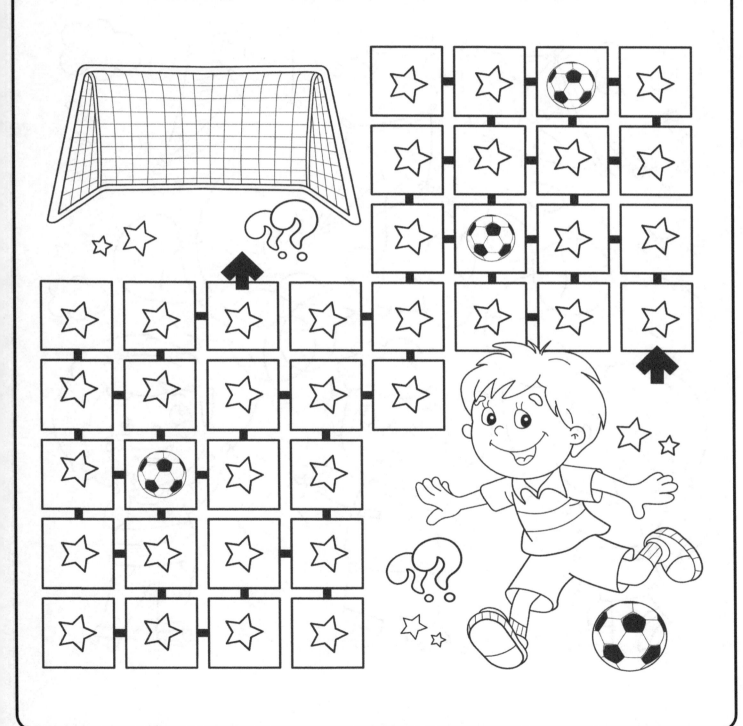

WHO IS HOLDING EACH KITE?

HELP THE PANDA GATHER THE BAMBOO!

GRAB A FRIEND . . .

CHOOSE THE RIGHT PATH!

PLAYER ONE _____

AND RACE TO WIN!

CHOOSE
THE RIGHT
PATH!

PLAYER TWO _____

COLLECT ALL THE LETTERS OF THE ALPHABET.

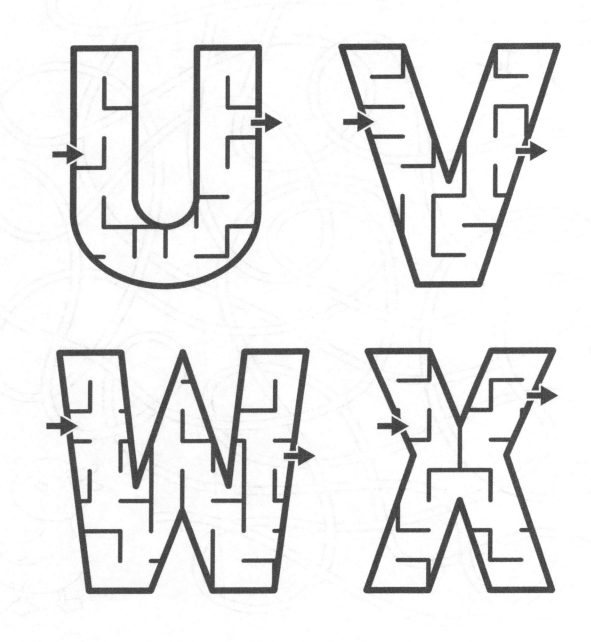

CAN YOU WIN IT IN A MINUTE?

START

FINISH

I DID THIS MAZE IN _____ SECONDS!

TRAIN CHALLENGE MAZE

☐ I MADE IT!

☐ I'LL KEEP TRYING!

HELP MAMA BIRD FLY HOME TO HER BABY!

CAN THE SUBMARINE SURFACE?

STAY ON THE STARS
TO GET BACK TO THE ROCKET!

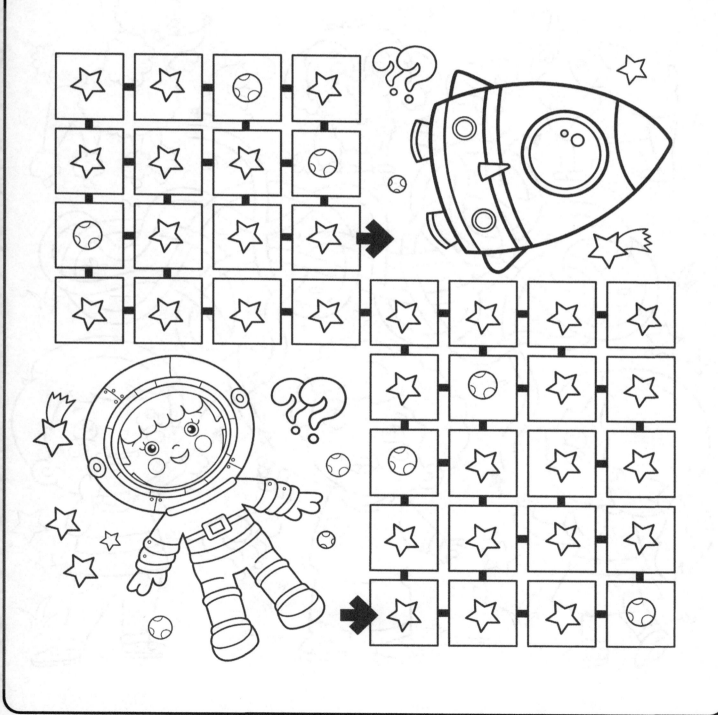

WHO OWNS EACH DOG?

CAN LITTLE DUCK KICK ALL THE SOCCER BALLS?

GRAB A FRIEND . . .

PLAYER ONE _____

PLAYER TWO _____

COLLECT ALL THE LETTERS OF THE ALPHABET.

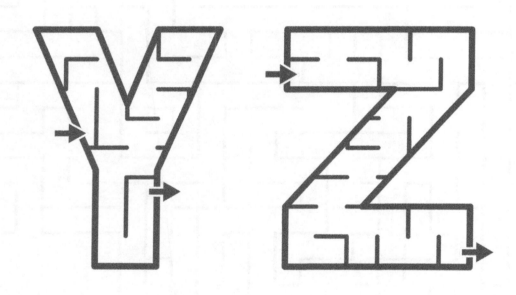

CAN YOU WIN IT
IN A MINUTE?

START

FINISH

I DID THIS MAZE IN _____ SECONDS!

HEDGEHOG CHALLENGE MAZE

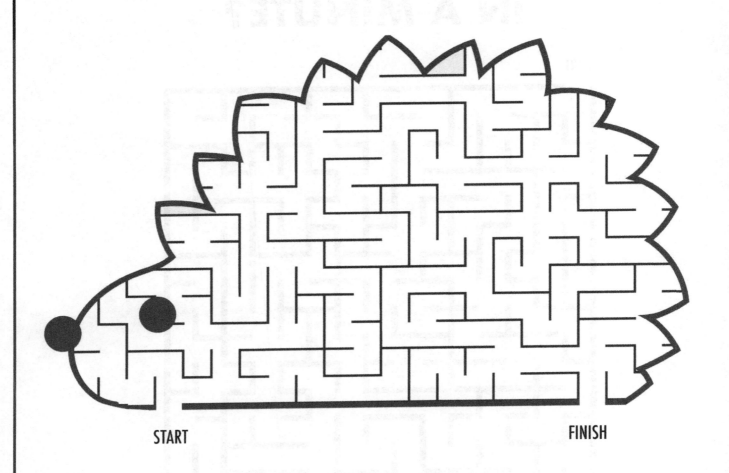

START   FINISH

☐ **I MADE IT!**

☐ **I'LL KEEP TRYING!**

HELP LITTLE DOG SNIFF HIS WAY TO THE BONE!

LAUNCH THE ROCKET!

CAN YOU WIN 1ST PLACE? STAY ON THE STARS!

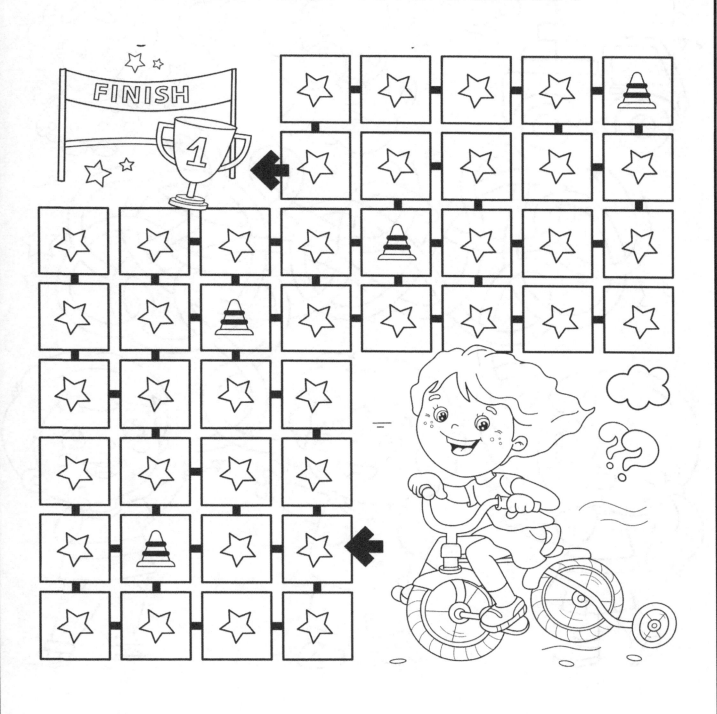

WHO LIKES EACH TOY?

HELP LITTLE RABBIT
PICK THE VEGETABLES!

GRAB A FRIEND . . .

START

FINISH

PLAYER ONE _____

AND RACE TO WIN!

START

FINISH

1

PLAYER TWO _____

GO FROM A to Z
USING ONLY STRAIGHT LINES.

START WITH THE LETTER A	R	E	F	G	O
	R	H	D	S	H	T
M	A	B	C	D	I	Y
K	N	M	L	K	J	B
A	O	V	W	X	E	N
Q	P	U	C	Y	END WITH THE LETTER Z
R	S	T	P	Z	

CAN YOU WIN IT IN A MINUTE?

START

FINISH

I DID THIS MAZE IN _____ SECONDS!

STAR CHALLENGE MAZE

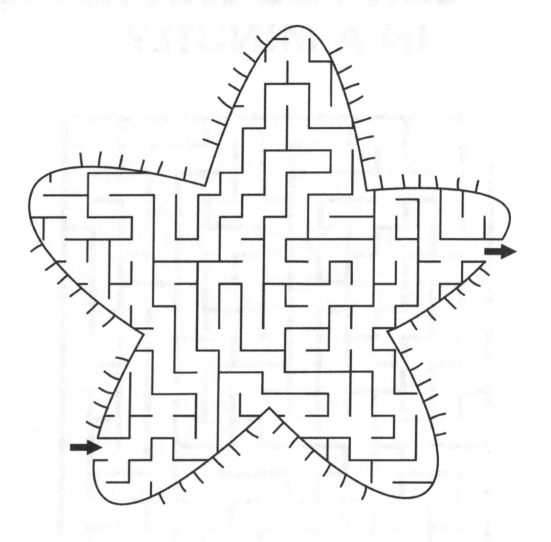

☐ I MADE IT!

☐ I'LL KEEP TRYING!

WAY TO GO!!

YOU'RE AMAZING!

FINISHED LEVEL 1

OF AMAZING MAZES!

Made in the USA
Monee, IL
17 February 2024

53669495R00046